Christina H. 5C

W9-CMU-945

WILDLIFE ADVENTURE SERIES

ARCTOS

Illustrations by JOSEPH CAPOZIO

the grizzly

RHODA LEONARD

HARR WAGNER PUBLISHING COMPANY   San Francisco

TABLE OF CONTENTS

IN 1758 the scientist Linnaeus named the Old World brown bear *Ursus arctos*. When that bear's cousin, the North American grizzly, became known, it was called *Ursus horribilis*. The name shows how people generally regarded grizzlies.

"Give a dog a bad name and you hang him" goes an old saying. Something like that happened to California grizzlies. People feared them, regarded them with horror, and killed them off. Grizzlies became extinct in California.

When I decided to write this book, I read everything I could find about grizzlies. I became acquainted with the grizzlies in the San Francisco zoo, even though they are not native Californians. I found that it is true that grizzlies are more vicious than black or brown bears, and sometimes they will attack a man without provocation. Yet they usually prefer just to be left alone. And I even found records of young grizzlies raised as household pets. I felt that this animal had been, quite literally, given a bad name.

A famous authority on grizzlies, Dr. C. Hart Merriam, apparently felt the same way. At any rate, he gave some of them new names. He named one type of California grizzly *Ursus arctos californicus*. The hero in this story has the same name, but I call him Arctos for short.

this is the story of that grizzly

ARCTOS the grizzly

1

FROM DEN
TO DANGER

IT WAS WINTER. The heavy fog that lay over the hilltops kept the sun from warming the brown slopes and ravines below.

Against the side of one hill there was a pile of dirt, half-hidden by scrubby oak and chaparral. It was such a pile as a miner might have made when tunneling his way toward gold. But this was California in 1835. There were no miners in the hills in those days. The cry of "Gold!" had not yet been heard. Indians, Spaniards, and Mexicans sometimes traveled by. American trappers may have made their way there. But neither Indians, Spaniards, Mexicans, nor American trappers had piled that dirt high. None of them had needed to dig a den in which to spend the winter!

A grizzly bear, digging with her big hooklike front claws, had dug out the dirt to make a hillside cave. The entrance to the cave was some three feet wide and four feet high. Just inside, a kind of entry hall reached nearly ten feet into the hillside. Beyond the entry hall was the warm, dry cave. Grass and dried leaves covered its uneven floor.

This circular space measured about eight feet across. Its five-foot ceiling would have given a human child room to stand up. But the children in the cave were not human children. They were tiny grizzly bears.

Covered with hair so fine that pink skin showed through, each of these small creatures was about nine inches long. None of the three weighed more than a pound. Yet some day they each might weigh a thousand pounds or more! They would be huge and terrifying. But now at two weeks old, their eyes still shut, they were almost like kittens. Like kittens they lay close to their mother, a mountain of fur that meant both food and warmth. Like kittens, too, they sometimes whimpered softly.

"Eu-wow-wow," came the tiny sound, first from one and then from another. But it was not a complaining cry. The three little cubs were warm and well fed. Arctos, his brother, and his sister were quite content with their lot. They were just trying out their voices.

The mother bear had moved into the den in November. The cubs were born in January. In all that time their mother had not left the cave. She had not eaten anything or had anything to drink. Most of the time she had been asleep. She was thinner now than she had been in autumn, but she still weighed more than four hundred pounds. Like her cubs, she was content to stay just where she was for a while longer.

More than a month went by. The cubs ate and slept and ate again. Their weight increased. By the time they were forty days old, it had doubled. Each of them weighed about two pounds. They gained a few inches in length, too. Their baby teeth began to grow. Most important of all, their eyes opened.

Not that there was very much to see. It was dark in the cave. They could see the shape of their mother's strong forelegs, which she could use as either legs or arms. They could see the outline of the hump between her big shoulders. But they could not see the color of her coarse fur, brown mixed with yellow, gray, and white, that made men call her "grizzly."

The color of the cubs, too, soon began to change from naked pink to grizzly tones. Their fur became long and thick and soft.

By mid-March the cubs had begun to move around. By now they were nearly as large as rabbits. Moving clumsily on their short legs, they sometimes bumped into one another. When that happened, they often tumbled over. This struck them as great fun. Soon they began to bump into each other on purpose. They rolled and tumbled all over the den. But they still headed back to their mother whenever they were hungry.

It was April before their mother really roused herself. Slowly she stretched her legs and lifted her head. With a great effort she lumbered to her feet. Planting her forefeet firmly in front of her, she stretched again. Her cubs watched in wonder as their great fur mountain moved.

Arctos, the eldest, moved close to her. But his mother was hungry, and hunger made her cross. With one great paw she sent Arctos sprawling. Then, walking with a rolling gait, she moved heavily along the entry hall. She stood a moment at the opening to the cave, her small black eyes peering at the daylight. Then she turned and lumbered back into the den.

Slowly she moved from one cub to another. She gave each one a not-too-gentle slap. With each slap went a low growl, almost like a cough. The message was clear to her cubs. It meant, "Stay here and behave yourselves."

Then, for the first time in their short lives, their mother left them alone.

It was a strange and frightening feeling. At first the cubs sought comfort from one another. They huddled together against the farthest wall of the cave. After a while the youngest one, the little she-cub, fell asleep. But the two males kept watch in the darkness. They did not play or tumble now. They lay still, peering toward the opening of the den, silent and waiting.

After what seemed a very long time, their mother returned. She seemed much better-natured. Now when Arctos came close to her, she did not send him sprawling. She lay down on her bed of grass and leaves so the cubs could have their dinner. The little she-cub woke up and moved over to her mother's body. Soon all three of them were fed and sleeping soundly.

The little bears awoke next morning to a feeling of excitement. Something seemed about to happen. The cubs sensed a restlessness in their mother. She hurried them through breakfast, and she would not let them play. Before they knew it, she was nudging them toward the entrance of the cave.

Outside, the day was clear and sunny. The cubs stood blinking in the bright light of this strange new world. They felt the pleasant warmth of the spring sunshine. Now for the first time they had a good look at one another.

For the first time each saw that the others had dark patches on their ears and paws. Each saw the circles of dark fur around the others' eyes. To a person seeing them there, so still and quiet, the cubs might have looked like teddy bears. Yet each had the flat forehead and shoulder hump that belong only to grizzlies.

They were not quiet for very long. Arctos began to climb the little hill above their cave. The others soon raced after him. At the top they all looked down. Below them was a little river, bubbling and churning over the rocks. Below them, too, was their mother, keeping a close watch on them.

Being a full-grown grizzly, she had little to fear from other animals. She could hold her own with most of them. But her cubs could not, and the cubs were her responsibility. Her eyes and ears were always alert for signs of danger. But most of all she used her keen sense of smell.

Now her nose quivered as she sniffed the breeze. All seemed well. She sat back on her haunches. In a gesture that looked almost human, she folded her forepaws across her grizzled chest. Even then she raised her head for one more careful sniff.

Arctos was watching her. He may have thought she looked comfortable. He may have thought it was a new kind of game. Anyway, he decided to follow suit.

Back he sat on his fat little haunches. Up went his forepaws across his chest. This was fun! Besides, it made him feel important.

While his younger brother and sister watched, Arctos decided to investigate the breeze. In careful imitation of his mother's movements, he raised his head and sniffed.

That did it! He lost his balance. The next thing he knew, he was rolling down the hill. Over and over he rolled, all the way to the bottom.

Before he was half way down, his brother and sister had decided to join the game. They chased after him down the hill. At the bottom they rushed at Arctos, slapping at him and holding him to the ground. Soon all three were tumbling in a tangle of dark paws. They crashed into thickets and slipped on loose rocks. Once they rolled very close to the river. Their growls were so fierce that all this seemed much more than play.

But after a while another sound was heard above their growling. It was their mother's low, choppy warning cough. The cough, followed by a few slaps from her paw, soon made them understand that it was time to go back to the den.

The other two cubs trailed obediently after their mother as she went inside. But Arctos looked around him and was reluctant to leave this bright new world. With so much to see and do out here, why should he go back into the darkness of the cave?

With only one backward glance, he dodged quickly into a nearby thicket. Then he stopped to enjoy his new-found freedom.

Birds sang and chattered in the trees above him. The spring air was so fresh that it almost tickled his nose. Whenever he moved in the sunlight, a funny dark shadow moved with him. He jumped toward it, trying to catch it. The outside world was a wonderful place to be!

Suddenly his eye caught sight of a little animal near a log not far away. It was about the same size as his brother and sister, but it looked nothing like them. It was black with a white V on its back. Still, since his brother and sister had gone back into the den, maybe this little animal would be his playmate. Arctos started toward it.

He had hardly gone six feet when something hit him so hard that he went sailing through the air. When he landed in a clump of bushes, his whole side was stinging from the blow. As he struggled to get back on his feet, his mother loomed in front of him.

In spite of her huge size, she had come out of the cave and upon him so quietly that he hadn't heard her. With one stroke of her paw she had sent him flying in a direction away from the skunk. Now Arctos had learned that his mother did not want him to go near this animal. He scrambled to get up.

But this was not the only lesson his mother wanted him to learn. As he started off toward the den, he caught another blow—this time on his fat little rump. The blow pushed him towards the den. Arctos was being punished for not obeying her first command to go inside. Now he practically galloped back to the den. Never had his legs moved so fast before!

The mother moved more slowly. She glanced at the skunk. Fortunately, it had felt no danger from either the mother or the cub and had not released its foul-smelling spray. The mother grizzly respected skunks and kept her distance when they were about. Assured now that this skunk had not been alarmed, she ambled toward the cave, even stopping on the way to catch an unwary lizard.

Meanwhile Arctos had gone as far back into the cave as he could go. When his mother returned, he was curled up quietly as if asleep. But his eyes were open and watching. He remembered the blows, and he wasn't quite sure that his punishment was over!

But the mother grizzly was satisfied that her discipline had already begun to teach him two things he must know—the necessity of obedience and that danger lurked outside the den. With a low grunt she called her cubs to her. This time they all came quickly.

2
A TRAP
IN THE FOREST

AS THE SPRING DAYS followed one another into summer, there were many changes in the cubs' way of life. The little bears grew in both size and knowledge. It seemed to Arctos that each day brought something new.

Sometimes it was food—sweet clover, a plant with tender shoots, or a nest of baby mice under a log.

Sometimes it was a game—a kind of hide-and-seek with his brother and sister, or playing with sticks or rolling stones.

Sometimes it was a skill—climbing trees and balancing on shaky branches, or being quick enough to catch a grasshopper or butterfly in mid-flight.

Life was fun, but all of the things they learned, even the games, would help them later when they were on their own.

But at this time of their lives, they still had much to learn. And their mother took her responsibility very seriously. She taught them many different ways to look for food. They learned to look under logs for grubs and lizards. They learned to thrust their paws into anthills. Then they would lick off the ants that covered the paws. The cubs liked this best of all. Crawling ants were fun as well as delicious! The cubs also learned to look for food under small sticks and stones. They turned the sticks and stones over gently, using one claw of the right paw, as all grizzlies do.

All the time, though, their mother kept a constant guard over them. She knew that a stray or wounded cub would be easy prey for a mountain lion, so she demanded strict obedience. When she didn't get it, the cubs felt the power behind her great paw. The little she-cub was more timid and didn't cause much trouble. But Arctos and his brother were more than once smacked six feet across the ground!

One day their mother led them downstream to where the little river widened into a pool. Here all four of them went into the cool water. The day was hot and the water felt good. Besides, it washed away the insects that hid in their fur and bothered them. Arctos and his brother and sister were not at all afraid of the water. Without even being shown how, they found that they could swim.

Soon Arctos became tired of splashing and swimming, and he found a tree branch that hung low over the water. When he caught it in his forepaws, it made a kind of swing. Always playful, he was delighted to have found a new game.

But his mother did not let him play very long. She had something else on her mind. She herded her cubs out of the water and along the riverbank again. They went until they reached a place where the water was not so deep and the river ran more swiftly. The mother bear waded in, but when the cubs started to follow her, she gave that choppy cough that warned them back. They were to stay on the bank and be quiet.

The little she-cub dozed off as usual, but Arctos and his brother stayed awake and watched. They soon grew bored. They were getting hungry, too. Arctos saw a fallen log not far away and wondered what would be under it. His mouth watered as he thought of grubs and insects and lizards. Maybe even mice. He glanced at his mother, back at the log, and at his mother again. But he had learned by now the punishment for disobeying, and he had too often felt the power of that big forepaw. He decided not to risk it.

Just then his mother made a quick motion toward the water with her paw. The next instant something shiny landed with a plop at Arctos' feet. It seemed to be alive. It flapped around but never got far away. Arctos put out a paw and touched the slippery skin. A wonderful smell reached his nose! Holding the flapping thing still, he dug his teeth into its middle. It was delicious! One more bite and the whole fish disappeared.

Arctos waited eagerly for his mother to perform the same trick again. But the next time the fish landed near his brother. It was the other cub's turn to taste the new treat.

When a third fish came sailing through the air, both cubs lunged for it. Pushing, clawing, growling, each one tried to get it for himself. Arctos struck his brother hard across the head. His brother returned the blow with bared teeth.

Suddenly, one after the other, each cub felt their mother's paw. They ran out of reach as soon as possible. Then they both sat licking the spots that hurt. Their mother stood guard over their little sister, who had been awakened from her nap by the growling. The little she-cub was now eating her first fish.

The mother stood in the stream almost two hours more. Without fighting, the cubs shared the fish she threw on the bank. Sometimes she kept a fine big one and ate it herself. But there was plenty for all, and they all ate their fill.

In fact, as summer turned to fall, they seemed to spend most of their time stuffing themselves. There were so many kinds of food they liked: fish, berries, plants, roots, grubs, ants, insects, snakes, lizards, mice. The cubs were still too young to catch most small animals, but their mother caught several ground squirrels for them. Once in a while, she would catch a rabbit.

They wandered far in the next few months—over hills, across small valleys, through thick chaparral and underbrush to other watering places and feeding grounds. Often they followed well-worn bear trails that their mother seemed to know. The cubs did not really like the bear trails for they were uneven and hard to walk upon. Hundreds of grizzlies for many years had come this way, and each adult had put his paws down in the paw prints of those who had used the trail before. Some of the big hind prints were ten inches deep. This did not bother their mother, who lumbered easily along, her own paws deepening the prints just a little bit more. But the cubs much preferred the wider hillsides because many of these trails were through undergrowth or thickets so dense that there was nowhere to walk but on the uneven ground.

Their favorite places were the oak groves where many grizzlies gathered to feast on the ripe acorns. There Arctos, his brother, his sister, and other young bears climbed the trees and shook down the acorns. Sometimes the cubs broke small branches from the tree and threw them to the adult grizzlies waiting below. Arctos did not understand why, but he soon learned that his mother and the other adults could not climb at all. They could stand on their hind legs and reach the lower branches of the oak trees. For a real harvest of acorns, though, they had to depend on the cubs.

Once, when Arctos was in an oak tree and his mother decided it was time to move on their way, she called him to come down. Arctos knew well that choppy cough, and he usually obeyed her command. But now he looked at his mother with his little black eyes and decided to stay where he was. She couldn't come after him, and for once he was safe from her heavy paw.

His mother seemed to know what was in his mind for she called him only once more before ambling off with the other two cubs. Moments later she and the cubs disappeared into a nearby thicket. Only one other grizzly was there at that time, and it soon moved away, too. Arctos was alone. He looked at the thicket where his mother had gone and wondered if she had kept right on going! All at once he didn't want to be in the tree any longer. He scrambled down the trunk and ran to the thicket. His mother and brother and sister were there waiting for him! But his cries of delight at finding them were cut short by the worst cuffing he had received in his whole young life. The next time his mother called him from a tree, Arctos reached the ground before she even had a chance to call a second time!

It was at this time that tragedy first came into Arctos' life. One day when they had stuffed themselves with acorns, the four bears settled down in a manzanita thicket for an afternoon nap. The she-cub lay close to her mother and stayed there, but after a while the two males grew restless. They began to investigate rocks and logs and brush nearby. The mother was only half asleep. She was watching Arctos, who had found a nest of yellow jackets and who was the one who usually got into trouble. The other cub had disappeared a moment before into some trees a short distance away.

Suddenly the air was filled with frantic squeals of terror. The mother grizzly got up and galloped toward the sound with a speed that belied her huge size. Arctos and his sister followed. The young cubs were curious and, at the same time, fearful.

The squealing seemed to have changed from terror to anger and back again to terror.

The mother stopped with a low growl, and the cubs stopped, too. The little bear was nowhere in sight. His cries seemed to come from under the ground. Arctos realized that somehow his brother had fallen into a deep hole. He went nearer the edge to look in, but his mother turned on him and slapped him hard—not only hard but almost savagely! Arctos and his sister moved back near some bushes to watch.

As their mother sniffed around the hole, she seemed to catch a scent that made her angry. She tore at the ground with her claws. The cries of the trapped cub only made things worse, for she knew she couldn't reach him without falling in herself. She bellowed with rage. Then, mad with fury and grief, she began to bite and claw at everything within her reach—bushes, the ground, and even the bark of trees.

CAPOZIO

The mother knew why she was angry. Not only was she helpless to save her cub, but she had caught the scent of man. And something in her past had taught her that man was her enemy. The little bears had caught it, too, just before their mother had pushed them away. Although their brother's cries and their mother's anger made them afraid, they had no reason to fear the scent itself.

They sensed only that something was wrong, while their mother sensed tragedy. The hole was a trap. Although she did not know it was an elk trap nor that it had been made by Indians, she did know that man had something to do with it. She knew there was no way to save her cub.

The mother's anger and cries of grief and rage went on till darkness began to fall. At last, wearily and heavily, she turned back to Arctos and his sister, who were still cowering beside the bushes. Slowly she began to lead them away.

As they followed their mother, the cries of the trapped cub became fainter and fainter behind them. At last the cubs could hear them no longer. But their mother stopped several times to look back and listen.

Arctos and his sister were hungry as well as tired. They would have liked to stop and eat, but their mother would have none of it. She kept them moving until they found a sheltered cave under some over-hanging rocks. She pushed the cubs into it and as far back as possible. It seemed to Arctos that she was more than usually rough. She commanded them to stay, and then she left and disappeared into the night.

Arctos sensed that she was going back to the trap.

She returned not very long after. When she had reached the trap, it was empty. She had followed the scent of man some distance, but it led her farther and farther from her other two cubs, who were still her responsibility. And so she had come back.

She slept heavily, but every so often, even in sleep, her huge body shivered and she gave a low growl.

She roused her cubs before dawn and led them from the cave. Hungry though Arctos was, he was not allowed to stop and eat till almost noon. They were traveling in a direction away from the trap. The mother was making sure that if they met any more danger, it would be far away from there!

3

YOUNG GRIZZLIES
ON THEIR OWN

FOR A VERY SHORT TIME, Arctos may have
missed his brother, but only when the little she-cub
was not willing to play with him. There were plenty of
other things to interest his little bear mind, and it is
probable that he didn't even remember. But the mother
grizzly kept an even closer watch on her two remaining
cubs during the following weeks of fall.

The mother and the two young ones spent most of
their time eating. They ate so much that they soon had
a thick layer of spongy fat beneath their skin. Berries
and acorns were plentiful, but the bears still liked
meat when they could get it.

One morning the mother lifted her head and sniffed the air with more excitement than she had shown for some time. She set off to follow the scent, the cubs trailing after her. Soon they came upon the carcass of a deer, freshly killed by a mountain lion. The big cat had just begun his feast. When he saw the grizzlies, he spat in anger. The mother called her cubs to stay very close behind her. Then, growling and baring her teeth at the cat, she approached slowly. The mountain lion slunk away before she came too near, spitting as he went. When he had reached a safe distance, he stopped and crouched down, eyeing the cubs hungrily. But the mother grizzly was watching, even though she had begun to eat.

The mountain lion circled them once or twice as if he were looking for a safe way to attack. The mother kept facing him all the time. At last she raised herself up, let out a kind of roar, then dropped to all fours, and lunged toward him. This was too much for the mountain lion. He was not afraid of most animals, and he would fight even a grizzly if he had to. But this one was larger than he. Also, she was a mother protecting her cubs, and he did not want to tangle with her. He was hungry, but food was not that scarce. He left the cubs with their mother, left the deer to the grizzlies, and bounded off to look elsewhere.

The mother and cubs had a good feast. This was a big deer and more than they could eat. Now the cubs were to learn another lesson.

When they had had enough, the mother dragged the carcass to where there was soft earth. She scooped out a shallow place and put what was left of the deer into it. Then she covered it all over with dirt, leaves, and twigs.

The mother was not hiding the deer from the mountain lion. His keen nose could lead him to it, anyway. Besides, he had been driven away and probably would not come back. Their mother was hiding the meat from the vultures and California condors that circled, ever watchful, in the sky. Great numbers of these birds would swoop down and pick clean the bones of any dead animal in less than an hour.

Arctos and his sister watched carefully and remembered. They had learned that the kill of a mountain lion made a good feast. They had learned that meat should be covered before being left.

The bears might have come back and finished the deer the next day, but food was plentiful at this time of year. They followed a bear trail that took them far away to other things to eat.

The bear family went into hibernation early that year. When they came out to their second spring, life had changed for Arctos and his sister. No longer were they cubs. They were not adult grizzlies, either, but they could take care of themselves quite well. Mother seemed different, too. She paid little attention to them now, and wandered off farther by herself.

The young bears stayed near each other, but they

roamed farther, too. They found their own feasts in the forest. Sometimes they did not get back to the den in the evening. They slept instead in any handy thicket.

Their mother did not seem to mind their absences. She stayed away a great deal of the time herself. After a while the young bears gave up going back to the den entirely. They never saw their mother again.

Arctos and his sister spent the summer together. They roamed the hills and valleys. By now, each was much heavier, stronger, and more able to take care of himself. The young female weighed just less than two hundred pounds, while Arctos already showed signs of being unusually large—a giant of his species. He weighed nearer three hundred pounds, and he was still far from being full-grown.

It was good to be so strong, but in the fall they found out that their growth had one disadvantage, too. They could not climb trees as they used to. The parts that we would call wrists had grown stiffer. Their claws no longer gripped the branches as they once had. Now when the acorns were ripe, the young bears could only stand on their hind legs and pull at the lowest branches. Sometimes they ate the nuts that had already fallen to the ground. Once, with a group of older bears, Arctos and his sister stood under the trees and waited for smaller cubs to harvest the high branches.

They followed bear trails and wandered freely from one feeding ground to another. Often they stood on their hind legs and clawed the bark of trees.

Occasionally they met other grizzlies. From time to time they found tree markings much higher than their own. These were claw scratches on the bark. The height told them that an older and larger bear used this part of the hills or woods as his range. But the older bears never bothered them. It seemed to be understood that while the bears were young, they were free to wander where they pleased.

Once they saw a fight between two full-grown males. Each one was fighting for the right to use that range as his own. Several times they met one old bear with a very bad temper. He had a torn left ear which was probably the scar of an earlier fight. He seemed monstrous as he raised himself to a height of nearly nine feet! He glared at the two young bears and growled, but he left them alone. Arctos did not know it, but he would meet this bear again some years in the future.

There was little danger that fall. The only animal that Arctos and his sister avoided was the skunk, and they were very careful not to annoy or surprise any they met. Very occasionally, men passed through these hills, but so far the young grizzlies had never seen a man.

They grew fat and enjoyed life and stayed out of hibernation as long as they could. But the days became gray and sunless, and the nights cold and wet. The bears found a snug dry cave under some overhanging rocks. It had a dense thicket in front that protected it from the wind. Arctos and his sister curled up together till the winter had passed.

As they slept, their hearts beat very slowly. Their breathing was light. Their bodies used up very little energy. They had enough fat stored up to last them till spring. Even as they became thinner, they grew in length. When they finally came out of the cave, they were young adults.

Each grizzly stretched in the warm sun. The heat went right through their fur and seemed to put new life into their muscles. It felt good to be back in the world again!

Now brother and sister no longer seemed to need each other. The female lumbered away in one direction, Arctos in another. The last family tie had been broken. Arctos was alone. His life was his own. From now on he would depend only on his own strength and his own wisdom. He sniffed the air happily as he wandered along. Sometimes he stopped and rolled in the grass just because he felt so good. It was spring, and the whole world seemed to be waiting just for him!

4
ARCTOS MEETS THE ENEMY

NOW ARCTOS' WANDERING really began. During the spring and early summer, he stayed in the hills, although he roamed farther than ever before. Food was plentiful wherever he went, and he felt strong and vigorous. Gradually his wandering took him down from the hills and into the long valley of the San Joaquin River. He saw many other grizzlies on his travels, and now, from time to time, he saw men, too.

As he crossed the valley and made his way over the next mountain range, he came upon vast ranches. The Spanish Californians called their ranches *ranchos*. Thousands of cattle grazed on the hills, and sometimes Arctos saw the Spanish cowboys, or *vaqueros*, riding by. Sometimes a ranchero and his family would be traveling to visit a neighboring rancho. And sometimes, when Arctos ventured near a large rambling ranch house and stopped to drink at a nearby stream, he saw many women there, washing clothes.

By now Arctos was able to recognize the scent of man. He had not yet learned at first hand how really dangerous man could be. Still, the scent made him uneasy. When his keen nose told him human beings were nearby, he was very careful. He did not have to go close to people or their houses in order to feast on their cattle. The lands of the rancheros stretched for hundreds of miles.

Among the cattle there were always a few that were old, weak, or lame. He could catch these easily. Sometimes he would attack a calf or strong young heifer, but he had found out that often this was not a wise thing to do. More than once he had been chased by a range bull that was willing to fight to protect the young or choice animals in its herd. Arctos was a match for any bull, but he did not enjoy fighting. There was no reason to fight when food was so plentiful.

During this time Arctos did have one fight, but it was not with a bull. It was his first face-to-face encounter with man.

Arctos came out of a thicket one day into a cleared space beside a river. The wind was blowing from him to the river so that he was surprised to see an Indian, his hands cupped, ready to drink. Arctos might have moved away, but the Indian heard a sound behind him and turned. The man jumped to his feet, his eyes wide with terror.

The Indians of that region had more than a physical fear of grizzlies. They believed that grizzlies had magical powers. Some Indians believed that grizzlies were the souls of wicked and evil Indians who had died. Others believed that grizzlies were the ancestors of Indians. Nearly all Indians of California both respected and hated these great beasts that had arms and could walk upright with a rolling gait like a man's.

Of course, Arctos knew nothing of all that. He knew only that this creature had risen to his feet. To Arctos this was a fighting stance.

The grizzly rose onto his hind legs. With a growl like low thunder, he brought his full weight down on top of the Indian. The Indian, even though half-paralyzed with terror, managed to grab his hunting knife. As he went down, he plunged it into the bear's shoulder.

The sudden burning pain turned Arctos' growing anger into rage. He closed his strong jaws on the Indian's arm. The bones broke like matchsticks.

The Indian must have fainted with fear or pain, for he lay limp and still on the ground. Arctos slashed at him once with his paw. Then, because his enemy did not move, he sat back for a few moments and watched. Next he pushed at the body once or twice. There was still no movement. He turned the Indian half over. Gradually, as he realized that his enemy was not going to fight back any more, Arctos lost his anger. Now he began to feel the pain in his own wounded shoulder more keenly, and he wanted to go under a bush and lie down.

Arctos glanced again at the still body of the Indian. The man-scent was strong, and the grizzly had no desire to eat this creature. He turned and lumbered slowly away. When the Indian became conscious again, he would be grateful to be alive, but would hate grizzlies even more.

Arctos found a shelter where he lay for a few days, licking his wound till it healed. At first he did not eat much, and lived on plants nearby until he felt like wandering again.

This time he went on through the hills and canyons until he came to the Pacific Ocean. He stood in wonder on the shore. Never had he seen so much water! It was not good to drink, but the air was fresh, and there was a delightful fishy smell that excited him. He stood on the beach and felt the waves wash over his paws, then swirl back like living things around his legs!

He followed the shoreline for over a mile, finding a number of dead fish that had been washed up on the sand. These were much larger than the fish he had caught in mountain streams, and their flesh had a sharp juicy flavor that he loved. When his eyes spotted one ahead of him on the sand, he bounded towards it and gobbled it up as if he had just found a kind of prize.

Then one moonlight night he came upon enough food to satisfy even his huge appetite. The carcass of a whale had been washed ashore. Four grizzlies were already there, and another came after Arctos had begun to eat. What a feast it was! There was enough for all. The bears stuffed themselves for several nights before each one left to wander on his way.

By now Arctos often traveled at night. He had found out that men could be dangerous—more dangerous than the Indian who had only cut him with a knife. The Spanish Californians often killed grizzlies because of the damage the bears did to cattle and crops. Men often went out with guns to kill a great many bears at once. At other times, the Californians captured bears for sport. On those hunts the men used rawhide lassos called *reatas*. Once, when Arctos had been feeding with several other bears, four horsemen rushed out from behind some bushes and lassoed one of the animals. One reata had come so close to Arctos that he had felt it touch his side as he escaped. He had had no experience with guns yet, but he had heard them in the hills. Even the sound was enough to make Arctos more careful as he roamed these lands where men lived.

Yet these same Spanish Californians on the ranchos often provided feasts for the bears. Sometimes the men would ride over the hillsides and round up hundreds of cattle. Days would be spent sorting and branding them. Only the choice and healthy new ones would be marked. When the cattle were let loose again, the scrubby unbranded ones were with the others.

Then men would ride over the hillsides once more. This time, however, they would kill the unmarked cattle so that they would not weaken the herd or eat pasture meant for the others. The carcasses would be left for the grizzlies, mountain lions, coyotes, condors, and vultures.

Sometimes, too, when there had been little rain, the rancheros feared there would not be enough grass for their valuable herds. So the rancheros would kill great numbers of the horses that grazed on these same hillsides. Their carcasses, too, were left for the wild animals.

But the best feast of all for the grizzlies was a *matanza*. "Matanza" is a Spanish word for slaughter. Every year, just before the Yankee ships came to trade, matanzas were held on all the ranchos. The ships brought supplies that the Spanish needed and left with cargoes of hides and tallow. Hundreds of cattle were killed, and only their hides and tallow were wanted. Perhaps a little of the meat might be kept for eating, but most of the beef was thrown into a nearby gully.

The first time Arctos came upon such a huge pile of good food, he stuffed himself for hours. But there was plenty for all the grizzlies that gathered there. There was plenty even for the mountain lions and coyotes that waited till the grizzlies had finished before taking their turns. There was even some left for the vultures and condors, who had to wait till last.

With so much food around, Arctos had no desire to go back across the mountains and big valley to the hills that had been his first home. He stayed near the coast and grew fat. When winter came, he did not hibernate as he had before. The weather here was warmer and, of course, there was always plenty of food. Once in a while, when he had stuffed himself more than usual, he did sleep for a few days at a time, but it was not the deep sleep of real hibernation.

As winter followed winter, Arctos grew bigger and stronger. At eight years old, he weighed more than nine hundred pounds. Standing on his hind legs, he could reach a height of more than nine feet. If he were not killed by his enemy, man, he would probably live twenty or thirty years more. In terms of grizzly life he was still a teen-ager, but already he was taller and stronger than many older bears. And he was still growing!

In spite of the warmer weather and good food in the lowlands, one spring Arctos found himself growing restless. He had no aches or pains. But somehow he did not seem to be enjoying life. Perhaps he was lonesome at last for his old home range far away. At any rate, he felt the urge to travel. He started off in the general direction of those hills. He had no definite plan.

He just kept going. He stopped only to rest when necessary or to eat when his hunger became too great. Food did not delay him much. The only things grizzlies will not eat are pine needles, frozen twigs, and human flesh, so there was always something on his way that Arctos could find.

After weeks of traveling, he came one day to a place that seemed familiar to him. A feeling of happiness went through him. These were his woods! With a kind of joy, he clawed at the pines and rubbed his back against them.

As Arctos roamed his old range, he found claw marks already on some of the trees. But when he stretched up, they were all lower than his own. Soon he began to find claw marks that were quite new, and he realized there must be another grizzly nearby. He growled as he put his own marks higher on the same trunk.

Just then an old grizzly appeared from behind some bushes not far away. Neither Arctos nor the other bear recognized each other, but this was the old bad-tempered grizzly with the torn ear, the same one Arctos had met as a cub. Old Torn Ear had grown older, and his temper had become even worse. He regarded this as his range. He did not want Arctos or any other grizzly nearby. On the other hand, Arctos was young and strong, and he had made up his mind he wanted this range, too. Both bears began to growl. They reared, they charged, they lunged at each other. Tearing, slashing, biting, each one tried to prove that he was the master.

The battle did not last long. Arctos was much the stronger of the two. He had lived well in the lowlands, and his trip to the hills had made his muscles stronger still. Also, he was young.

Old Torn Ear's strength, decreased by age and his recent hibernation, was no match for the younger bear's. He fought gamely, but he knew when he was beaten. Before either animal was badly injured, Old Torn Ear ended the contest. He turned and ran. Arctos watched as he disappeared from sight.

Often, during the next few weeks, Arctos chased off other full-grown male grizzlies that dared to trespass on his land. Then one bright June day, there came a grizzly that Arctos did not chase away. A thick-furred female, half his age, entered his domain as though it were her own. And Arctos welcomed her. He liked the warm brown color of her coat with its tips of grizzled silver. He liked the way it changed to darker shades toward her head and feet. He liked the way that light and shadow seemed to ripple along her back with every movement. To us she might have seemed a matted, shaggy, homely creature. But to Arctos she was beautiful.

Arctos had found a mate.

5
CAPTURED!

ARCTOS AND HIS MATE roamed together during the weeks of early summer. They did not wander far. They kept within the boundaries of Arctos' chosen range. The wooded hills provided plenty of food. The bears ambled along slowly and let the warm sun penetrate their thick coats.

About mid-July, however, the honeymoon began to come to an end. The female seemed restless and less impressed with Arctos than she had been. Arctos, too, seemed to be getting bored. There were even times when a certain wisp of breeze or drifting scent would remind him of the lowlands. He was beginning to get lonesome for his other home.

One evening the female wandered away by herself. Arctos let her go. He made no attempt to follow her. It was of no interest to him that his mate would be looking for a safe dry den where she could spend the winter. Nor that, about January, she would give birth to his cubs. Adult male grizzlies have no use for small cubs and sometimes kill them if they get the chance. Arctos was tired of his mate, and he turned the other way, not even watching as she left him. It did not bother him at all that he would probably never meet her again.

Soon Arctos began to wander far beyond his range. He left the high hills and headed back to the lowlands. These were the rolling hills and the valleys near the coast where men lived. Arctos did not want to see the men, but he did want the things he found near them. He remembered such things as beehives, corn fields, potato patches, and thousands of cattle. Best of all he remembered those delicious feasts where the cattle were already killed for him!

By September, he had reached the clover fields of a long lowland valley. He felt so happy that he lay down and rolled among the fragrant blossoms. Next, he ate as many as he could of the tender leaves and sweet ripe heads. And when he had eaten so much that he could eat no more, he lumbered off to a nearby thicket to rest.

Had Arctos known what was taking place only a few miles from him, he might not have rested so well. He had come again to the ranchos of the Spanish Californians, and, on this particular rancho, preparations were being made for a grizzly hunt.

Unlike the Indians, these men did not respect the grizzly, and they had much less fear of him. They resented the way he killed their cattle, stole their bees and honey, and even attacked their horses. But they liked to use the grizzly for sport. Riding their horses, they would close in on a grizzly and lasso him with their reatas. The reatas were very strong. They were made of hide that had been dried in the sun, soaked in water, and cut into long strips about half an inch wide. Four of these strips were then braided together. When a reata was finished, it was as thick as a man's little finger and might be sixty feet long. At one end was a noose with a slip knot. Great skill was needed to capture a huge, vicious grizzly if no weapon was used but the reata. Sometimes, after the men had proved their skill by capturing a grizzly this way, they would kill the animal.

Yet sometimes they saved the grizzly for another one of their sports. This was the bear-and-bull fight. A full-grown grizzly and a strong bull would be put in a ring or kind of arena. They would fight until one of them won. Often both animals, even the winner, had suffered serious injuries by the time the fight ended. Today we would consider this pastime too cruel to be a sport, but in the days of Spanish and Mexican California, it was very popular. Even after California became a state of the United States, it continued for a while.

The Spanish Californians on the rancho near Arctos had their reatas made and ready. They had even chosen their horses. For the horses, too, had to be trained to do just the right thing at the right time. Now there was only one more preparation to make. A couple of cowboys, or vaqueros, rode to a clearing which happened to be not very far from where Arctos was sleeping. They brought with them, at the end of a tether, an old and weak horse. In the clearing, with a quick slash of a knife, one of them killed the horse. Then, working together, the vaqueros cut open the animal. Wearing gloves so that he would not leave too much of his human scent, one vaquero scattered the insides of the animal all around the clearing. The other cut off a hindquarter and tied it, with the tether, to his saddle. Then, mounting his own horse, he rode slowly round and round the slain beast, dragging the hindquarter over the ground. Each time around he rode in a wider circle. Finally almost every inch of the clearing carried the scent of horseflesh.

Satisfied, the vaqueros untied the hind quarter and placed it near the rest of the carcass. They covered the whole thing with leaves and bushes to hide it from the condors. Then, their work done for that night, they rode back to the ranch house.

Meanwhile, Arctos awoke. Tired from traveling the day before, and stuffed with clover from the meadow, he had slept through part of the night. But now he was rested and ready to eat again. As he sat back on his haunches and sniffed the air, the predawn breeze brought him the scent of a feast. He followed his quivering nose to the clearing, about half a mile away.

It did not take him long to reach it. When he arrived, another grizzly was already there. The other bear moved over to make room for him. The carcass was far more than they could eat at one meal. When they had had enough, they re-covered the carcass and went their separate ways.

Arctos marked the spot in his memory. He would return the next night for another meal. He ambled back towards his thicket. He ate a few tender shoots on the way, but let a snake go right by him without bothering it. It was good to be where there was so much food that he could eat only what he liked best! Arctos lay down heavily. He stayed there, sleeping and dozing, the whole next day.

Late in the afternoon, before Arctos awoke, six men rode towards the clearing. Two were the vaqueros of the night before. The other four were important rancheros. One of them owned all the hills and lands nearby; the other three were visitors from neighboring ranchos. The four rancheros carried reatas. The silver ornaments on their clothes and their saddles sparkled in the rays of the late afternoon sun.

The men rode to a clump of trees a hundred yards beyond the hidden bait. From that position they could not see the clearing, but they would know when a bear entered it. A sudden stiffening of their horses' bodies would tell them the instant that a bear arrived.

The bear, on the other hand, could not detect their presence. The men had chosen a place where the breeze blew away from the bait, not toward it. No scent of man or horse would be carried to the feasting grizzly.

Sitting easily in their saddles, the rancheros waited. Dusk settled gently over the land. The moon rose, becoming a bright ball of silver in the sky. A soft breeze rustled the branches above the waiting men. All else was silence.

Suddenly, every horse grew tense. Their ears pricked up, their heads were thrown back. Horses are terrified of grizzlies, but these horses were well trained. Their eyes were wide in the sockets, but the frightened beasts made no sound.

Arctos had come back for a second night's feast. The other grizzly had come back, too. They uncovered the carcass and began to eat, unaware that anyone was nearby.

One vaquero pressed his knee ever so slightly against his horse's side. The horse moved quietly out of the trees, just far enough to give the vaquero a view of the clearing. The rancheros, their eyes glued to the vaquero, tightened the grip on their reatas. Still they waited. The vaquero and his horse moved silently to one side. Then with a gesture of his hand the vaquero motioned the others forward. He had watched the two grizzlies uncovering the bait. They were completely in the open. Now was a good time to strike!

With a sudden bound, all four rancheros rushed their horses into the clearing. The startled grizzlies immediately tried to run away.

"Get the big one!" a vaquero shouted in Spanish. It was unnecessary advice. The rancheros were headed straight for Arctos.

Only the rancheros would do the roping. The vaqueros would wait excitedly in the background, shouting encouragement.

The most important ranchero was in the lead. As soon as he was close enough, about fifteen paces from Arctos, he sent his reata sailing. Arctos was caught around the neck. Horse and rider worked as one to keep the lasso taut.

As soon as Arctos felt the pull, he roared with rage and fear. Up he went on his hind legs, growling savagely.

Almost immediately, another lasso, from another direction, caught his right foreleg. Arctos tried to run. He tried to follow the second bear, now out of sight in a thicket. The two reatas jerked him back. Then he tried to charge a horse and rider. The reatas tightened again, pulling in opposite directions. Arctos could go nowhere. In spite of the leather that was choking him, he roared even louder than before.

Then he found there was something he could do. He sat back on his haunches and began to pull at the reata that was on his foreleg. Horse and rider pulled in the other direction, but Arctos' strength was so great that he felt the noose loosen a little on his leg. Paw over paw, he pulled. The horse was drawn nearer. If only Arctos could bring the animal within reach, he could split its whole side open!

But the hope was short-lived. A third reata caught the grizzly's other foreleg. Now the three rearing horses jerked him to the ground.

Even lying on his back, Arctos writhed and fought and roared. Dust rose all around him. But he was outnumbered. The fourth reata caught his hind legs— both of them!

A great shout went up from all the men, mingling with the uproar from the captured bear. Now the four horses stood their ground, keeping all reatas taut. One of the vaqueros dismounted and walked toward the bear, lasso ready. His approach sent Arctos into a new frenzy of writhing and roaring. But the four horses kept the big bear helpless.

When the vaquero was very close, Arctos tried to lunge at him. The vaquero's lasso caught the grizzly right around the jaws. Around and around the vaquero wrapped the braided leather. Now Arctos could not even roar. Arctos, once proud monarch of the wilds, was a helpless prisoner.

At that moment the other vaquero approached. In his hand was a broad-bladed knife!

6

IMPRISONMENT

EVEN THOUGH ARCTOS could not move, his muscles strained as the vaquero drew near. Fear and hate both surged through his great body as he kept his eyes on the approaching enemy.

Just then one of the rancheros called out. "Wait!" he cried in his native Spanish. "This animal is too big and too fine to kill. He's a fighter. Let us keep him for the bear-and-bull ring on Sunday."

Murmurs of agreement came from the other rancheros. The eyes of both vaqueros brightened as they thought of the sport that lay ahead.

And so the vaquero put his knife away, and other preparations took place. First, the noose around Arctos' neck was loosened and then removed. Now at least he could breathe more easily.

Next, the reata around his hind legs was released. With a quick surge of hope, Arctos kicked one leg free. But immediately the reata tightened around the other leg. Before he could do any damage with his free leg, it was caught again in another tightening noose.

The reatas that held the bear's four legs were each tied to a different tree. Arctos was now spread-eagled on his back. He could not open his mouth, but deep growls came from his throat. The men gathered around, laughing and talking as they looked their prisoner over. The grizzly's bright black eyes stared back at them with loathing. He kept straining at his bonds, but the braided leather held. He was extremely uncomfortable stretched out on his back, but he could not move.

Then one of the vaqueros rode away. He was gone for some time. When he returned, he was carrying the hide of a big bull. Long ropes were attached to it. He spread the hide on the ground near Arctos.

Working together, the vaqueros got the hide underneath the helpless bear. With rawhide cords they tied all four of the bear's legs together. Untying the reatas from the trees, they tossed the free ends onto the hide beside Arctos. Then they lashed him to the bull hide.

The rancheros waited until the ropes from the hide had been fastened securely to the vaqueros' saddles. Then they rode away in triumph. To the vaqueros was left the job of hauling Arctos to the pueblo where the bear-and-bull fight would be held.

That journey was torture to Arctos. As he was bumped and dragged along, through canyons and across dry stream beds, he was vaguely aware of the moon shining down upon him. He could hear the wind sighing in the trees and smell the familiar earth smells heavy in the damp night air. These were things he had known all his life. They were all around him, but he was no longer free to enjoy them. What had happened to him? He was bruised, and he ached in every muscle. But the pain was hardly worse than the humiliation. He was puzzled, hurt, and angry, all at the same time.

Perhaps it was his anger that kept his spirit alive during that terrible journey. Sometimes the vaqueros, riding side by side, sang a song or talked to each other. At each sound of a human voice, Arctos shuddered with rage. Fresh strength, born of anger, flowed into his great body.

It was daylight when the small procession reached the pueblo. The rancheros had been there for some time. They had been celebrating the capture and arranging for the coming fight.

Now, while Arctos stiffened in fear, many people crowded around him. There were vaqueros and rancheros and two men who were not dressed as the Spanish Californians were. These were Americans, and their clothes were made of hides. One had boots made from the paws and lower forelegs of a slain grizzly. The human scent was overpowering, but Arctos could neither fight nor run. So he retreated into silence—a fearful, sullen, watchful silence.

The ties holding the bear to the bull hide were cut loose. Eager hands seized the reatas that still clung to each of the bear's legs. Each reata was fastened, securely but not tautly, to a different tree. With one swift motion a daring vaquero untied the bear's great jaws. At the same time another one unbound the stocky legs. Both men darted out of reach as Arctos rolled over and scrambled to his feet.

Arctos still could not escape, but at least he could move his muscles. He could open his mouth. He could take a few steps now, and he could see what was going on around him.

The big bear was tethered in the shade of some large trees. A few feet away was what seemed to be a large square with a wooden fence around it. There was a gate with wooden bars through which Arctos could glimpse the inside of the fenced-off square. In the other direction stood a church and some low adobe buildings. Beyond them, in the distance, were the great brown and green hills.

Arctos was at one end of the pueblo's central plaza. The fenced square had been arranged especially for bull-and-bear fights. They were often held on Sundays and saints' days, after the people came from church.

Arctos had been captured on a Friday evening. He had spent many long hours, painfully bound, being dragged over rough earth and sharp rocks. In all that time he had not even had a drink of water. Nor did anyone think of giving him one now. The only thought of most of the people crowding around seemed to be to torture him. Coming as close as they dared, they poked at him with long sharp sticks. When he roared and snorted with rage, they laughed delightedly. Arctos snapped his big jaws at the closest spectators, but they always stayed just beyond his reach. Although his tethers were loose enough to let him move, he could not go far in any direction.

The day became hot, and to Arctos it seemed endless. He clawed and bit at the tethers for a while, but the tough leather did not yield. At last, thirsty, weary, and without hope, he lay down in silence. He rested his shaggy head wearily on his forepaws.

A little girl in the crowd had been watching Arctos with wide and sympathetic eyes. At last she said something to her older brother, a boy of about twelve. The boy nodded and ran off. In a few minutes he was back, carrying a clay pot filled with water. The boy set the pot on the ground, but he dared not place it close to Arctos. He went away again and came back with a long wooden paddle. Using the paddle, he inched the pot along the ground until it was within reach of the bear.

The crowd had fallen silent when the boy began his task. When he pulled back the paddle, they waited expectantly to see the bear lumber to his feet and drink.

Arctos was longing for water. He eyed the few drops that had spilled over from the pot. He got to his feet slowly. Moving cautiously, he started toward the clay container. He almost reached it. Suddenly a shrill feminine voice called out in Spanish, "There he goes! He's going to drink it!"

The sound of that human voice angered Arctos. He hated man! And even the clay pot was strong with man's scent. With one vicious slap of his right fore-paw, he broke the pot into a dozen pieces. The cool water ran over his paws. He knew how good it would have tasted. But he lumbered back a few steps and lay down again.

He lay there all day long. By sundown most of his tormentors had gone away. They would be back to-morrow to tease the bear again before the fight.

Only two vaqueros were left in the plaza. They would stay in their saddles all night long. They would be ready should Arctos somehow manage to loosen his tethers and escape.

The sun sank from sight, leaving the sky a fiery orange red. Then, in the glowing dusk, two small shadowy figures appeared. The little girl and her brother were back again. This time each of them was hugging a pot of water. They spoke to one of the vaqueros guarding the bear. He laughed good-naturedly and nodded.

Cautiously the boy did exactly as he had done before. He put the pot on the ground, then pushed it with the paddle. This time the pot came so close that Arctos could reach it without getting up. With one big paw he knocked it over. But he was not quite so angry now, and the pot did not break. The spilled water trickled toward him. Still, he would not even lick up the moisture while anyone was looking!

The boy who had brought the water seemed disgusted. He turned to go away. He did not want to shove a third pot toward the bear. But the little girl insisted. She argued with him. At last he gave in and pushed the third pot along the ground. This time Arctos let it stay there. The children watched for a while, then left. Much later, in the middle of the night, Arctos drank the water gratefully.

Maybe the drink helped him. Somehow, in spite of his aching muscles and the scent of human beings still strong around him, Arctos dozed. But before his eyes closed, he raised his head slightly to look at the distant hills—those hills that had been his home. Perhaps, now that the people had left, Arctos felt some faint return of hope.

7

THE
BEAR-AND-BULL FIGHT

ARCTOS STIRRED RESTLESSLY as the sun rose. He wanted to stretch. He wanted to exercise his stiff, cramped, aching muscles. But no matter which way he moved his giant bulk, one of the leather ties pulled him back.

As soon as the people began to gather, Arctos gave up. He lay down sullenly again, not even looking at his tormentors.

Among the crowds of people soon filling the plaza were the rancheros who had captured the grizzly. They came to inspect their captive and to see that the arena was in readiness.

64

Within the big arena was another fenced-off area. This would be where the fight would take place. The bull was already in his pen in a far corner of the inner enclosure. Arctos could not see it from his prison among the trees.

Bright flags draped the fences and a high platform opposite the gates. Gaily dressed women and children would watch the fight from the rows of seats on the platform. Most of the men would stay on their horses in the space between the inner and outer fences.

As the crowd milled about, one man lurched forward, coming quite close to Arctos. He was an American, one of those recent comers called gringos by the Californians.

The gringo was holding a long pointed stick. "He's got size, all right," he announced in a loud, unpleasant voice, shaking the stick at the bear. "Let's see if he's got any nerve to go with it."

Reaching out with the stick, the gringo gave Arctos a sharp jab in the ribs. "Come to life, you lazy lump!" he yelled.

The jab did not really hurt Arctos, except for a momentary sting. But it made him furious. With a deep growl, he grabbed savagely at the stick. The man let go abruptly, and Arctos snapped the wood in two.

The holiday crowd yelled its delight. This had all the makings of an exciting show!

Someone handed the man a heavier stick. He stepped forward more carefully this time, taking cautious aim. At that moment a ranchero galloped up behind the crowd. Leaping from his horse, he shouldered his way through. With one hand he caught the gringo's arm and spun him around.

"Let the beast alone, *señor*," the ranchero said in accented English. "Do not wear out his anger before this afternoon."

The American pulled back his arm as if to strike the newcomer. But the people sided with the ranchero. He was one of those who had captured the bear in the first place. The crowd persuaded the American to calm down. Finally the gringo shrugged his shoulders in disgust, then shuffled away.

Soon most of the crowd was turning away, too— some to heed the ringing of the churchbell, some to place bets on the outcome of the fight.

About three o'clock that afternoon, the sleepy silence of the plaza was broken by the clanging of a gong. Crowds of people began pouring through the gate into the fenced enclosure. Women and children climbed to the platform beyond the inner square. Men on horseback were lining up just inside the larger, outer fence.

Almost no one was left near Arctos now. Only his guards, two other vaqueros, and the children who had brought him water were still there. The little girl wanted to give him some more water, but the guards shook their heads impatiently. With her brother pulling her along by the hand, the little girl followed the others through the gate.

The guards were dismounting now. Each of them went to a tree where a reata was fastened. The two other vaqueros stationed themselves beside the other two trees. Then, splendid in silk and silver, the four rancheros who had captured Arctos galloped into view.

Arctos hated all men, but he growled in anger to show that he hated these men most of all. Each horseman headed for a tree where a vaquero waited. At a signal, each vaquero, with a lightning motion, loosed the reata and thrust it into the waiting hands of a ranchero. Working together perfectly, the rancheros tightened the reatas just enough to force Arctos to his feet. Then, judging their distance carefully, the horses, with the growling captive in their midst, pranced through the wide gate to the fenced-off square. The second gate, to the second enclosure, was open, also. Men, horses, and Arctos all entered the fighting arena.

The crowd roared its approval. The horsemen bowed toward the stands, but they did not ease their hold on the tight reatas.

A vaquero on foot darted through the gate and ran directly to Arctos. Stooping swiftly, he tied one end of a twenty-foot rawhide cord around a hind leg of the bear. He tossed the other end to another man, perched on a rail above the bull's pen. Then he left as quickly as he had come.

The man on the rail leaped lightly into the bull's pen for a moment. When he emerged and perched on the rail once again, he was no longer holding the rawhide. He had tied it to one of the bull's forefeet. He waved a signal to the horsemen.

Suddenly, all together, each man on horseback cut loose the reata with which he was holding Arctos. In one swift rush, horses and men bounded through the open gate. The inner gate banged shut behind them. Arctos was alone—apparently untethered. At least, there was no pull on his legs any more. With amazing speed, using teeth and claws and forepaws, he was able to rid himself of the now loose reatas. Only the rawhide cord on one hind leg remained. He found that tightly knotted. It would take a little time to work it loose.

Then, just as he started to bite and pull at it, a snort from the direction of the bull's pen attracted his attention. He had not noticed the pen before, nor was he particularly interested in it now. Trying to get the rawhide off his leg was much more important.

Nor did the bull seem to be interested in the bear. Even when the bars were removed from its pen, it had given that one snort and then just stood there staring. Someone from the stands called out, and the man on the rail gave the bull a hard, cruel kick with his spurred boot. The animal snorted twice, stamped, and charged into the arena.

Another roar went up from the crowd as the bull entered. It was a beautiful animal. Its dark, glossy coat was marked with white. Its horns were sharp and even. Its muscles rippled as it moved.

The bull seemed confused at first and apparently didn't even notice Arctos. It pawed the ground a few times. Then it began to run around the enclosure near the fence as if trying to escape.

But the bull had gone only part way around when Arctos felt the tightening of the rawhide on his leg. He pulled sharply at the cord with his forepaws. The pull jerked the bull's legs. The huge, snorting animal went sprawling on the ground. The force of its fall sent Arctos toppling backwards.

Now anger flared in both the beasts. Both scrambled to their feet. Both were further enraged by the shouting of the crowd. The bull charged, not at Arctos, but at the stands. Women and children screamed as the bull came towards them. But the charge did not last long. The rawhide cord, with the bear's great weight behind it, pulled the bull up short. Once more the big beast went sprawling on the ground.

This time, when the bull got to its feet, it turned toward Arctos. Somehow it sensed that the bear was responsible for holding back the charge. The crowd fell suddenly silent. This was what they had all been waiting for!

Arctos, sitting on his haunches, was working frantically at the cord. He was still not paying much attention to the bull. The sudden silence made him look up. There, just across from him was the bull, head down, ready to charge!

Arctos rose on his hind legs. This was his usual fighting stance, but this time it was a mistake. The bull hit him with tremendous force. One of its horns smashed into his ribs. The charge knocked the breath out of Arctos, but he was not badly hurt. With his sharp claws he ripped at the bull's sensitive nose. The bull bellowed in rage and pain.

Now Arctos was on his back with the bull above him. He grabbed again at the bull's nose, this time with his strong jaws. He held on. Next he grabbed his opponent around the neck with his forepaws. The bull struck at Arctos a number of times with its hind feet. Arctos shook the bull savagely by the nose. Then, rolling and scuffling, the beasts changed places. Now it was the bull that was being held to the ground. Blood streamed from its nostrils. Flesh hung from its head and shoulders where the bear's claws had dug in.

At last, with a mighty wrench, the bull broke free and started to run. Before the bleeding beast was out of reach, Arctos seized its hind foot between his teeth. Arctos hung on and was dragged for a short distance.

Then the bull, snorting, breathing heavily, and half-blinded by blood, stopped. The two animals were just in front of the enclosure gate. Arctos loosed his hold and reared back, ready for another charge.

But at that exact moment Arctos made a discovery! The rawhide cord was no longer on his leg. He was no longer fastened to the bull—or to anything! Somehow, during the struggle or while he was being dragged, the knot had loosened and the cord had slipped off. Arctos did not even think about how it had happened. All he knew was that for the first time in days he was free!

With one tremendous lunge, he crashed through the wooden bars of the inner gate. The startled horses between the fences reared and almost bolted. The outer gate was open, and Arctos galloped through it, knocking a horse and rider to the ground as he went by.

The fallen horse and rider blocked the gateway for one precious moment. That was just long enough. With an amazing burst of speed, Arctos put yards between himself and his human enemies. Within seconds he was beyond the reach of the lassos that the surprised horsemen tried to get into throwing position.

On and on he bounded! He passed the trees where he had been held captive. He passed the low adobe buildings and empty church. He was beyond the pueblo almost before the crowd knew what had happened. Across a small clearing, he went crashing into a thicket, and there, in its protection, he found an ancient grizzly trail that led toward the hills.

Behind him, the crowd was in an uproar. Rancheros and vaqueros were busy keeping a tight rein on their rearing horses. Two men lassoed the bleeding bull, hustling it back to its pen before it, too, could get away. Some of the women were screaming, and two fell fainting in the stands. Children clutched at their mothers' skirts and added their cries to the confusion.

But high in the wooden stands, one little girl stood silent and apart, her eyes shining. It was the child who had brought Arctos water. Now, as long as she could see him, she watched the bear in flight.

"Go! Go!" she whispered softly, her small fists tightly clenched. "Go back to the hills and live for years and years! Never come back here again and be caught. Run! Run and be free!"

Of course Arctos could not hear her. But it so happened that he did exactly as she said. And being a very strong bear who had learned a lesson, he may well have lived to a ripe old age. Perhaps some of his descendants are among the few and precious grizzlies that still roam some western parks and forests. In any case, his memory is preserved—in the state flag, state seal, and state history of his native California.

EXERCISES

Chapter One
FROM DEN TO DANGER

Choose the right ending for each of these sentences.

1. The setting for the story of Arctos is
   a) California today.
   b) California over one hundred years ago.
   c) Alaska.

2. Arctos was born during the
   a) summer.
   b) winter.
   c) autumn.

3. The story of Arctos takes place during the
   a) twentieth century.
   b) Gold Rush.
   c) nineteenth century.

4. When Arctos was born, his mother had had
   a) nothing to eat for six months.
   b) no food or drink for forty days.
   c) no food or drink for about two months.

5. Bears like Arctos were called grizzlies because
   a) they had bad tempers.
   b) of their coloring.
   c) they had stubbly beards.

6. The cubs' mother communicated with them by
   a)   whistling at them.
   b)   making noises and gestures they understood.
   c)   making marks in the sand with her claws.

7. A sound made often by the mother bear was
   a)   very much like a sneeze.
   b)   a kind of cough.
   c)   a long, lonesome howl.

8. Arctos did not want to go back to the den because
   a)   he was afraid of the dark.
   b)   there was so much to do outside.
   c)   it was too crowded.

9. The animal Arctos saw was dangerous because it was
   a)   so much bigger than he was.
   b)   armed with a weapon Arctos could not match.
   c)   poisonous.

10. The mother grizzly punished Arctos because
    a)   disobedience could lead to danger.
    b)   she was stronger than her cubs.
    c)   she was bad-tempered.

Chapter Two
A TRAP IN THE FOREST

Choose the right ending for each of these sentences.

1. Most of the games the cubs played
    a) were team sports.
    b) helped to develop skills.
    c) were things they did to tease their mother.

2. Swimming was a skill the cubs never
    a) quite mastered.
    b) dared to try.
    c) needed to be taught.

3. The cubs' mother caught fish with
    a) a net made of twigs.
    b) her paws.
    c) the branch of a tree.

4. The mother bear punished her cubs by
    a) making them go hungry for a long time.
    b) leaving them alone for a long time.
    c) slapping them with her paws.

5. Grizzly trails in California were
    a) a day's journey apart.
    b) used mostly by traveling Indians.
    c) marked with deep pawprints.

6. When grizzlies gathered to feast on acorns,
   a) they all climbed the trees to harvest the nuts.
   b) only the young ones climbed the trees.
   c) only a few adult grizzlies climbed at one time.

7. When Arctos disobeyed and stayed in the tree, his mother
   a) went away and left him.
   b) sent another bear up after him.
   c) only pretended to leave him.

8. The tragedy in Arctos' life at this time was that
   a) his brother was trapped.
   b) his sister was trapped.
   c) Arctos was trapped.

9. Although several things made the mother angry, the main one was that
   a) she caught the scent of man.
   b) she could not save her cub.
   c) the cub was crying.

10. The mother had not followed the man-scent far because she
    a) lost the trail.
    b) was tired after a hard day.
    c) did not want to leave the other two cubs.

Chapter Three
YOUNG GRIZZLIES ON THEIR OWN

Choose the right ending for each of these sentences.

1. During the next few weeks, Arctos
   a) grieved for his brother.
   b) probably forgot his brother.
   c) found another male club to play with.

2. That fall the three bears developed
   a) a thick layer of spongy fat.
   b) stiff wrists.
   c) fast speed.

3. The mountain lion watched the cubs because he
   a) wanted to keep them away from the deer.
   b) was hungry for meat.
   c) thought the cubs might share the feast.

4. The mother grizzly
   a) paid no attention to the big cat.
   b) let the lion eat when she had finished.
   c) drove the lion away.

5. Grizzlies covered meat with dirt and twigs to
   a) keep it out of the hot sun.
   b) make it more tender.
   c) keep it from scavenger birds.

6. The following spring
   a) each bear went its separate way.
   b) the mother separated from the two cubs.
   c) the mother and she-cub left Arctos alone.

7. As the young bears grew heavier, they
   a) found it harder to climb trees.
   b) became bad-tempered.
   c) began to fight with smaller bears.

8. By fall Arctos weighed about
   a) one hundred pounds.
   b) three hundred pounds.
   c) a thousand pounds.

9. Arctos and his sister looked for a den when
   a) the weather began to get cold.
   b) they realized their mother had left them.
   c) they saw two big grizzlies fighting.

10. When they came out of hibernation as young adults,
    a) Arctos fought with his sister.
    b) Arctos and his sister left each other.
    c) the two bears still traveled together.

Chapter Four

ARCTOS MEETS THE ENEMY

Choose the right ending for each of these sentences.

1. The Spanish Californians who owned vast ranches
    a) were called ranchos.
    b) were called rancheros.
    c) were called vaqueros.

2. Arctos would not fight the range bulls because
    a) he was afraid of them.
    b) grizzlies never fight.
    c) other kinds of food were plentiful.

3. Arctos attacked the Indian because
    a) he hated the man-scent.
    b) he remembered his brother.
    c) he thought the Indian was going to fight.

4. The Indian's life was saved because
    a) he fainted and lay still.
    b) Arctos just wanted to teach the man a lesson.
    c) he won the fight with his knife.

5. Arctos liked the seacoast because
    a) there was so much water.
    b) he found dead fish on the sand.
    c) the waves tickled his feet.

6. When Arctos found the whale,
    a) he ate alone.
    b) several grizzlies shared the feast.
    c) he had to fight other grizzlies for the meat.

7. Arctos usually roamed at night because
    a) it was cooler.
    b) he liked the moonlight.
    c) it was safer.

8. The main reason for a matanza was to
    a) collect hides and tallow for trading.
    b) slaughter cattle for eating.
    c) kill weak cattle.

9. Arctos did not hibernate in the lowlands because
    a) all the dens were taken.
    b) he did not want to be captured as he slept.
    c) the weather was mild and food plentiful.

10. When he fought Old Torn Ear, Arctos
    a) wanted to kill him.
    b) wanted Old Torn Ear's range for himself.
    c) was just playing.

Chapter Five
CAPTURED!

Choose the right ending for each of these sentences.

1. When Arctos and his mate parted company, they
   a) had a savage fight.
   b) probably never saw each other again.
   c) were both lonely for a long time.

2. Male grizzlies were known to
   a) kill cubs if they had a chance.
   b) help the mother care for her cubs.
   c) have three or four mates at a time.

3. Arctos returned to the lowlands because he
   a) liked to be near men.
   b) wanted the foods he found where men were.
   c) wanted to meet other grizzlies.

4. Reatas were made from braided
   a) ropes.
   b) rawhide.
   c) reeds.

5. To capture a grizzly with reatas took great
   a) wealth.
   b) skill.
   c) height.

6. Today Americans do not hold bear-and-bull fights because
   a) such fights are cruel and unfair.
   b) there are no more fighting bears.
   c) bulls are more valuable than bears.

7. For bait, the vaqueros
   a) scattered acorns.
   b) killed an old horse.
   c) tied a calf to a tree.

8. The most important thing in roping a bear was to
   a) catch him around the middle.
   b) hold the lasso loosely.
   c) tighten the lasso promptly.

9. The vaqueros
   a) were not important to the success of the hunt.
   b) lassoed the bear but did nothing else.
   c) performed dangerous feats during the hunt.

10. The vaquero with the knife was probably going to
    a) kill Arctos.
    b) cut him free.
    c) cut a branch to tie him to.

Chapter Six
IMPRISONMENT

Choose the right ending for each of these sentences.

1. The rancheros saved Arctos for the fight because
   a) they were sorry for him.
   b) he had a loud growl.
   c) he was an exceptionally fine, strong bear.

2. The hide of a bull was used to
   a) haul Arctos to the pueblo.
   b) make Arctos angry at all bulls.
   c) keep Arctos warm before the fight.

3. Arctos was kept a prisoner in the plaza for
   a) more than twenty-four hours.
   b) a week and a day.
   c) almost a month.

4. Only one person in the crowd thought of
   a) poking at Arctos with a stick.
   b) giving the grizzly water.
   c) untying Arctos so he could run away.

5. The water pots the boy brought were made of
   a) clay.
   b) dried hides.
   c) heavy iron.

6. Arctos knocked over the pots of water because he
   a) did not like water.
   b) hated the smell of clay.
   c) was angered by the crowd and the man-scent.

7. The boy gave Arctos a third pot of water
   a) when the vaqueros asked him to.
   b) because he felt so sorry for the animal.
   c) because his sister was so insistent.

8. The girl wanted Arctos to have water because she
   a) liked to watch him hit the pots.
   b) wanted him to be in good fighting trim.
   c) was sorry for him.

9. When Arctos was very tired, he
   a) lay with his head on his forepaws.
   b) rolled over on his back.
   c) snored.

10. The bear-and-bull fight was to be held on
    a) Friday.
    b) Sunday.
    c) a date to be announced later.

Chapter Seven

THE BEAR-AND-BULL FIGHT

Choose the right ending for each of these sentences.

1. The fighting bull was kept in
   a) a green field not far away.
   b) a pen inside an enclosure.
   c) an iron cage.

2. The rancher stopped the American because he
   a) hated all Americans.
   b) wanted to save Arctos for the fight.
   c) did not like to see animals hurt.

3. Californians called Americans
   a) greasers.
   b) cowboys.
   c) gringos.

4. Some people left the plaza in order to
   a) have breakfast.
   b) go to church.
   c) go to tease the bull.

5. The American who teased Arctos was
   a) very brave.
   b) very intelligent.
   c) very thoughtless.

6. The bear-and-bull fight took place in the
   a)   cool of the evening.
   b)   morning.
   c)   afternoon.

7. Ladies sat on the platform, but most men
   a)   stayed on horseback.
   b)   walked around the bull's pen.
   c)   sat on the fences around the enclosure.

8. The man above the bull's pen
   a)   waved his hat at the bull.
   b)   caught the cord and tied it around his waist.
   c)   signaled to the riders that all was ready.

9. The bear and the bull
   a)   could hardly wait to get at each other.
   b)   thoroughly enjoyed fighting.
   c)   were goaded by men to fight.

10. Arctos escaped to the hills because
   a)   he was a tricky bear.
   b)   the bull let him go.
   c)   there was so much confusion.

11. The grizzly is the official
    a) mascot of the San Francisco Giants.
    b) state animal of California.
    c) guardian of Yosemite National Park.

THE BEAR FAMILY

ALL BEARS everywhere belong to various branches of one family. The family name is *Ursidae*. Among the numerous cousins are the black bear, *Ursus americanus;* the polar bear, *Ursus maritimus;* the brown bear of Europe and Asia, *Ursus arctos;* and the grizzly, sometimes called *Ursus horribilis*. There are other cousins, with other names, in Africa, India, and South America. The brown bear of Europe and the grizzly bear of the western United States are closely related. All the others appear to be more distant relatives.

GRIZZLY BEAR

All types of bears carry certain strong family resemblances. Most of them are large, stocky, and somewhat clumsy looking. Their tails are short, their legs stout, and they have five toes on each foot. Their forelegs are fashioned rather like our arms, and in walking they use the whole sole of the foot, just as we do. All bears have two layers of fur, a finer one underneath the rather shaggy outer layer.

Though there are many likenesses among members of the bear family, there are also many differences. Some have longer or coarser hair than others. Some have shorter or longer claws. The shape of the teeth varies from one group to another. One of the chief differences, however, is in their coloring. The polar bear, for example, is a yellowish white. Only the soles of its feet are black. Brown bears and black bears are

BLACK BEAR

POLAR BEAR

colored as their names imply. Grizzlies are more brown than black, but both their brown and their black hairs are mixed with gray or yellow-white or both. There are wide differences of coloration from grizzly to grizzly, even among those living in the same area.

Some researchers have made sharp distinctions between the California grizzly and those of other western areas. Those distinctions, of course, are not nearly so great as those between grizzlies generally and their neighbors in the West, the black bears. First and foremost is the difference in coloring—a difference reflected in the very term "grizzly," since grizzled is defined as sprinkled or streaked with gray. Another difference is in size. Grizzlies grow to be much larger than black bears. Records are unfortunately very scarce, but it is probable that some California grizzlies weighed twelve hundred pounds or more. Their great weight kept them from climbing trees, a feat that black bears perform easily.

THE GRIZZLY'S FOREHEAD IS SLIGHTLY CONCAVE.

The grizzly's forehead is slightly concave, the black bear's slightly convex. Another distinctive grizzly characteristic is the shoulder hump, which gives the grizzly the appearance of added height.

There are recorded instances of fights between black bears and grizzlies. In those parts of California that the two groups mutually inhabited, however, they seem generally to have achieved a form of "peaceful co-existence." While there appears to have been no warm family feeling between them, neither is there evidence of a family feud. It is true, however, that as the grizzly population declined, the black bear population became more widespread throughout the state.

At one time grizzlies probably ranged over the western part of North America all the way from Alaska and Canada to Mexico. Because grizzlies could and did eat almost every kind of food, they could live almost anywhere except the most barren deserts. Intelligent and adaptable, they quickly adjusted to almost any

THE BLACK BEAR'S FOREHEAD IS SLIGHTLY CONVEX.

kind of environment. Those in the far north, for example, hibernated when the weather was cold and food of any kind hard to find. In milder climates, only females hibernated, and then only when they were bearing or caring for cubs. The usual pattern was for the mother to stay in hibernation until the cubs were a few months old. The family then emerged for the summer, but went back into hibernation together for the second winter. The third winter the cubs hibernated together, but without their mother.

Mating usually took place about the fourth or fifth year, but mates did not stay together long. When they separated, the female went in search of a den for the winter. The male often traveled a considerable distance to a different range area.

Although their thick coarse fur, layers of fat, and rolling gait made them look even clumsier than most bears, California grizzlies were surprisingly agile. For limited distances they could gallop as fast as a horse. Their great forepaws could move with great speed and dexterity, yet their long curved claws could be used almost as daintily, one at a time, as a person's fingers.

Many people have tried to describe the voice of the grizzly. No two people have ever quite agreed about it. Perhaps this is because grizzlies tend to be far less vocal than other animals. They usually make no sound at all unless they are hurt or frightened, or are communicating some definite message to their cubs. When they do feel the need to express themselves, it may be with a cough, growl, snort, roar, or a long low sound that seemed to hunters like "mough-ou-ough."

Not only did grizzlies tend to keep quiet, they also minded their own business most of the time. Most of the early residents of California complained that the grizzly was a vicious beast that attacked men, horses, or cattle without provocation. An observant few insisted, however, that the attacks were always provoked, either by fear, hunger, wounds, or the memory of some previous encounter with man. Certainly the grizzly did seem to be possessed of a certain fierce pride. They were frequently known, for instance, to refuse to eat or drink in captivity.

GRIZZLIES USE THEIR
LONG CURVED CLAWS
LIKE FINGERS.

Some grizzlies, both cubs and adults, were captured and trained as pets. One famous trainer, "Grizzly" Adams, trained some grizzlies to help him hunt other grizzlies! He also trained them to act as pack animals. Generally speaking, although he was well clawed on more than one occasion, Adams regarded grizzlies as docile, good-natured animals.

GRIZZLY ADAMS

GRIZZLY BEAR BOOTS

Left to their own devices, the grizzlies seemed to enjoy getting their food in a variety of ways. They were excellent fishermen. They were not averse to putting on a show, if necessary, to bring some curious cattle within their reach. Lifting up heavy logs to get the grubs from underneath them seemed to be regarded as a pleasant pastime.

Although grizzlies rarely, if ever, killed a deer or elk, they sometimes fed on the carcass of one killed by some other animal or by man. Only human carrion failed to attract them. There is no recorded instance of a grizzly eating human flesh, although grizzlies tore many a person limb from limb.

Perhaps no other animal has been mentioned so frequently in connection with the winning of the West. The earliest explorers, starting with Coronado in the sixteenth century, described grizzly bears. Early in the seventeenth century Viscaíno and his party watched grizzlies feeding on a whale carcass at Monterey. The Portolá expedition reported "groups of bears" near San Luis Obispo in 1769. Indian legends dating back for centuries were rich in grizzly lore. Jedediah Smith, Frémont, Lewis and Clark, and Bidwell were among the many Americans who wrote of encountering grizzlies.

Although the Indians feared grizzlies and sometimes killed them, they did not really reduce the grizzly ranks. The Spaniards and Mexicans made great inroads, occasionally using guns to diminish the number of bears, but more often hunting for sport with reatas. In spite of such activities, however, the number of grizzlies increased, if anything, during the Spanish and Mexican periods because of the additional food provided by the herds of cattle.

It was only during the second half of the nineteenth century, when Americans took over California, that the grizzly's doom was sealed. The Americans built ingenious traps strong enough to withstand even the onslaught of an enraged grizzly. Some Americans even resorted to poison to destroy the bears that molested their livestock. The principal weapon against the beasts, however, was the single-shot muzzle-loading rifle. The ranchers usually went hunting in groups, since the first shot rarely killed a grizzly. While the first man was reloading, the second fired, and so on until the bear was dead or helpless. Even so, grizzly hunting was a dangerous undertaking that resulted in much mutilation and many deaths.

STEEL GRIZZLY TRAP

Some aspects of the bear-and-bull fights changed as more and more Americans moved to California. They began to keep the captured bears in iron cages and to attach chains instead of rawhide cords to the feet of the fighting animals. The Americans also brought advertising ballyhoo to the promotion of the fights. Signs and posters and pre-fight processions helped arouse fevered enthusiasm. Betting became an important feature of the activities, especially at the mining camps that sprang up with the Gold Rush.

As more American families moved west, however, the attitude toward bear-and-bull fights began to change. Public opinion began to disfavor the cruel sport. Los Angeles banned bear-and-bull fights in 1860. Some other parts of the state continued to tolerate them, though, even into the 1880's.

Inevitably, the more people there were in California the less room there was for grizzlies. They became an almost constant threat to the settlements and so were hunted relentlessly. No foresighted conservationist group came to their rescue by proposing a wilderness refuge for them. No provision whatsoever was made for preventing their extinction, and by the early 1900's every grizzly had disappeared from California.

Few grizzlies remain anywhere in the country today, but there are some survivors in zoos and in such protected zones as Yellowstone National Park. Reminders of those colorful early residents of California are numerous, however. There are a few fragmentary specimens in museums of natural history. Statues of grizzlies may be seen in many public places, such as the

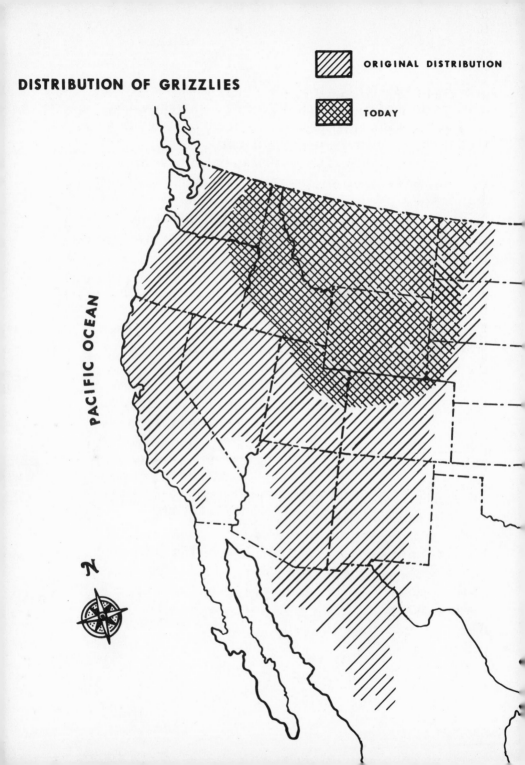

DISTRIBUTION OF GRIZZLIES

ORIGINAL DISTRIBUTION

TODAY

PACIFIC OCEAN

N

State Fair Grounds in Sacramento. The grizzly, as the official emblem of California, appears on both the state flag and the state seal. California sports teams include the Bears and the Bruins. Place names, such as Grizzly Peak, Grizzly Springs, Grizzly Bluff, and Bear Valley, recall the days when the shaggy beasts were a living part of western history.

Of course there could be no place for grizzlies in the teeming midst of present-day California. It is regretable, however, that no attempt was made to protect at least one group of California grizzlies, that this unique branch of the bear family might not have vanished from the earth.